Becoming Royal

Teachers and the Students

Meet Princess Sofia and the characters of the Royal Prep School with the help of your stickers.

Fauna

Merryweather

Flora

Princess
Sofia

Robin

Clover

Mia

Peekaboo!

Princess Sofia and her friends are playing a game of peekaboo! Can you tell who is who from the close-ups? Use your stickers.

A Princess Painter's Palette

It's time for Princess Sofia's painting class! Use your stickers to discover who and what she will be painting!

The Royal Garden

Princess Sofia attends the Royal Prep Academy. Decorate the scene with your stickers.

Royal Numbers

Sofia has been playing with her collections. Use your stickers to figure out how many things she has in each collection.

A Delicate Puzzle

Complete the lovely image of Princess Sofia with the help of your stickers.

Royal Rows

The kingdom of Enchancia is full of beautiful things! Use your stickers to complete the pattern in each row.

Sweet Scene

Sofia adores her animal friends! Make the bottom scene match the one on top with your stickers.

Princess Training

Princess Pastimes

While waiting for class to start, Amber and Sofia play tic-tac-toe. With a friend, play your own game below.

Studying Sorcery

Match the stickers to the shadows to figure out who conjured up each crystal.

Flick of a Wand

Sofia and her friends are making a sudden appearance in the library. Use your stickers to make them magically appear.

Hectic Halls

Between classes, the halls of Royal Prep are filled with people! Complete the scene with your stickers.

Mini Mansion

Amber and Sofia have worked together to make a model of a mansion for class. Help them finish it with your stickers.

The Royal Prep Academy

by Amber & Sofia

Hiding Places

Playing a game of hide-and-seek at the castle is fun! Use your stickers to help Merryweather find everyone.

Gem Game

Sofia has a lot to learn about her new friends. Help her give each new friend a gem in his or her favorite shape and color.

Pretty Puzzle

Sofia is learning to walk like a princess. She's using a book to practice her posture. Use your stickers to complete the scene.

Royal Life

A Regal Family

Use your stickers to help Sofia complete her family photo album, and meet all the new members of the royal family.

My Family

Queen Miranda

King Roland

Princess Sofia

Princess Amber

Prince James

Sizing Up!

Help Sofia organize some of the objects around the castle by placing them in order from smallest to largest.

Memory Match-Up

As a princess-in-training, Sofia has a lot to remember! There are two of each image below. Help Sofia find the pairs.

A Royal Ball

Sofia certainly isn't used to so many fancy occasions—especially ones for her! Decorate the scene with your stickers.

Precious Objects

Just as Sofia loves the Amulet of Avalor, everyone has things that are important to them.
Use your stickers to match the objects to each of the characters.

Color Confusion

Uh–oh! Everyone's clothes are the wrong colors! Use your stickers to change the colors back to what they should be.

Complete the Looks

Sofia has a whole new wardrobe, with accessories to match! Match everyone to the accessories that complete their outfits.

Spot the Changes

Use your stickers to discover the differences between the top and bottom images.

Dance Like a Princess

Day in the Life

Princesses are busy! Use your stickers to place Sofia and her friends in some of the places she will be visiting today.

Partner Up!

Everyone is learning to dance in pairs. Pair the partners with your stickers.

Decorated Dance Floor

Everyone is looking forward to the ball. Help make the top ballroom ready for dancing by decorating it like the bottom one.

Twirling and Whirling

Sofia is having fun in her dance class. Decorate the scene with your stickers.

Dance Steps

Every dance has its own unique steps. Use your stickers to complete the dance charts. Then, create your own dance!

Waltz

Salsa

Your Own Dance

Who's Who on the Dance Floor?

Dance class can get pretty busy. Can you tell who's dancing by their clothing?

Fancy Fine Fans

Princess Amber is helping Sofia look her best by decorating her fan. Decorate your own fan along with them!

Musical Chairs

Sofia and her friends are playing musical chairs. Use your stickers to see who is left standing when the music stops.

Royal Recreation

Near and Dear

Everyone has people and things that are special to them. Use your stickers to see who and what is dear to the characters below.

Outfit Options

A princess must have the right outfit for every occasion! With your stickers, match everyone to the event they're dressed for.

Visiting

Bedtime

Ball

Flying Derby

Royal Ceremony

Shiny Stones

There are lots of jewels that come with being a princess! Help Sofia decorate her new tiara and shoes.

A Lively Palace

Look at all the people who have gathered in the palace! Use your stickers to decorate the scene.

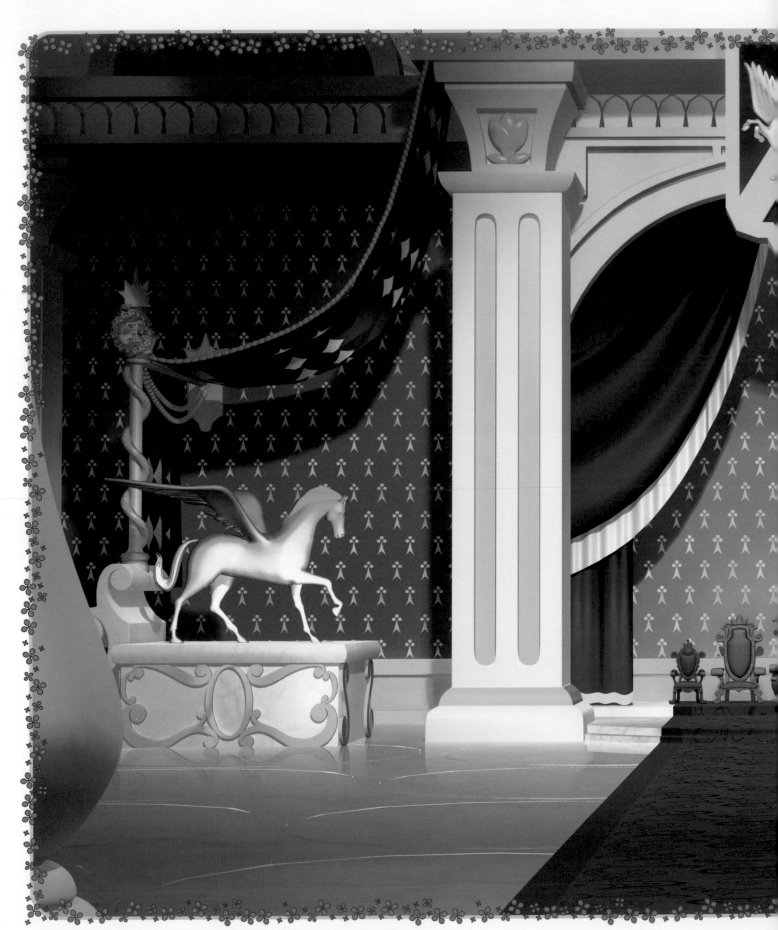

Outdoor Classroom

It's a beautiful day for an outdoor lesson! How many of each of the pictures in the ovals can you find in the scene? Place the right number sticker on the shadows in the bigger ovals.

Study Period

Match your stickers to the shadows to reveal who and what is in the library and who and what isn't.

Terrific Teatime

Tea pouring is one of the many skills princesses and princes must learn! Use your stickers to match each student to their tea set.

Eye Know You!

Match your stickers to the shadows to see which set of eyes belongs to which Enchancia character.

Royal Games

Prized Puzzle Pieces

The busy queen and princess still find time to play together. Help Sofia and her mother solve the puzzles.

Treasure Map

Sofia is making a treasure map for Prince James! Help her finish it by putting in the clues that will lead him to the hidden treasure.

Two of a Kind

The royal twins aren't the only pair in the castle. Pair up the similar objects.

Step Games

Sofia has gathered everyone for a game of tag! Use your stickers to find out who's playing.

92

93

94 95

96

Shape Search

Someone has put ribbons all over the castle. Help decorate them with gems that match the shapes on each ribbon.

A Busy Royal Bee

There's lots to do around the palace! Use your stickers to see some of the different things Sofia does in a day.

Hide & Seek

Help Baileywick find everyone by showing him their hiding spots with your stickers.

Fancy Flying Horses

Sofia was the first princess to join Royal Prep's Flying Derby team. Use your stickers to make the flying horses really royal!

Becoming a Princess

New Friends

Sofia has made lots of new friends! Use your stickers to meet some of them.

Pretty Books

Help Sofia decorate her book with your stickers.

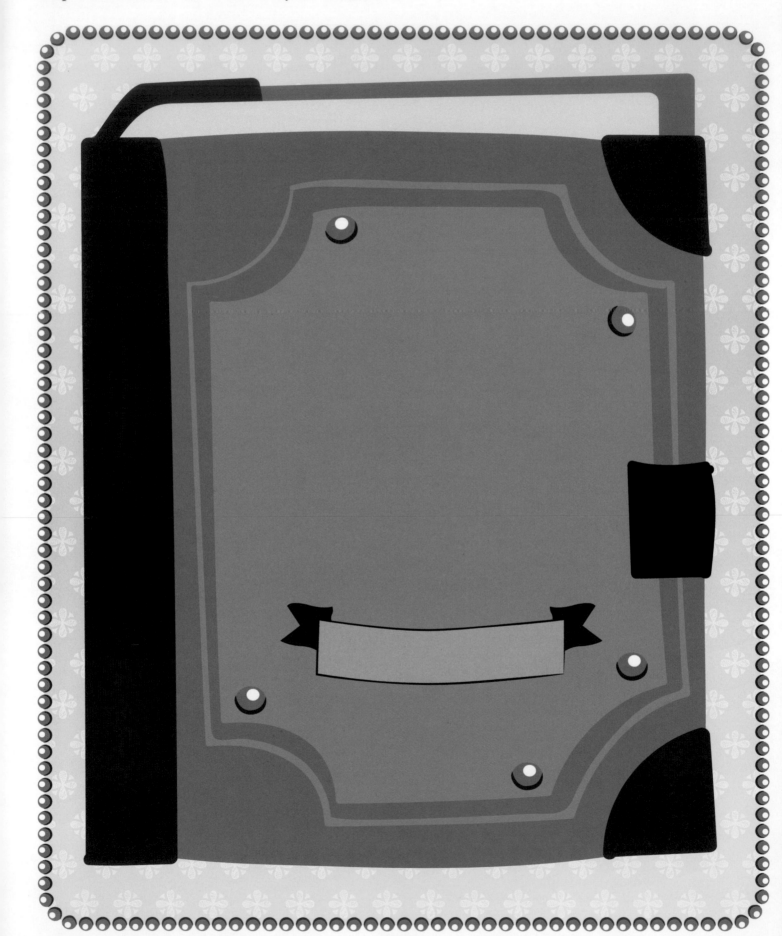

Party for a Princess

Sofia is having a party! Use your stickers to see what will make it extra special.

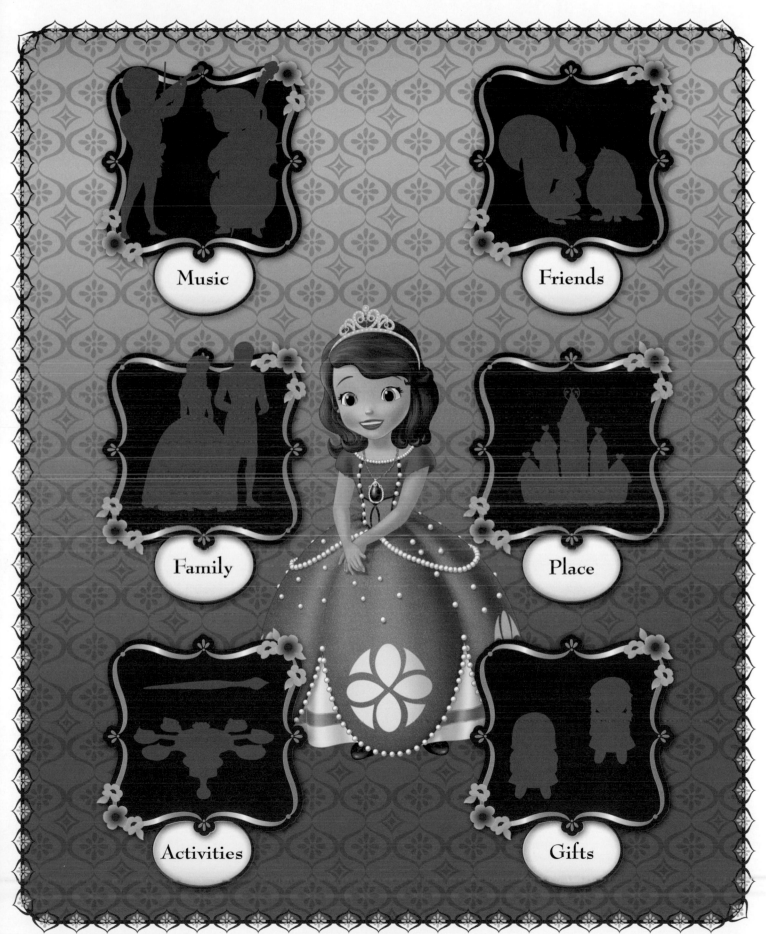

Music

Friends

Family

Place

Activities

Gifts

Princess Celebration

On the morning of Sofia's party, she gets a grand wake-up call. Decorate the scene with your stickers.

Color Chart

Enchancia is a colorful place! Group together the things that are the same color.

Yellow

Pink

Purple

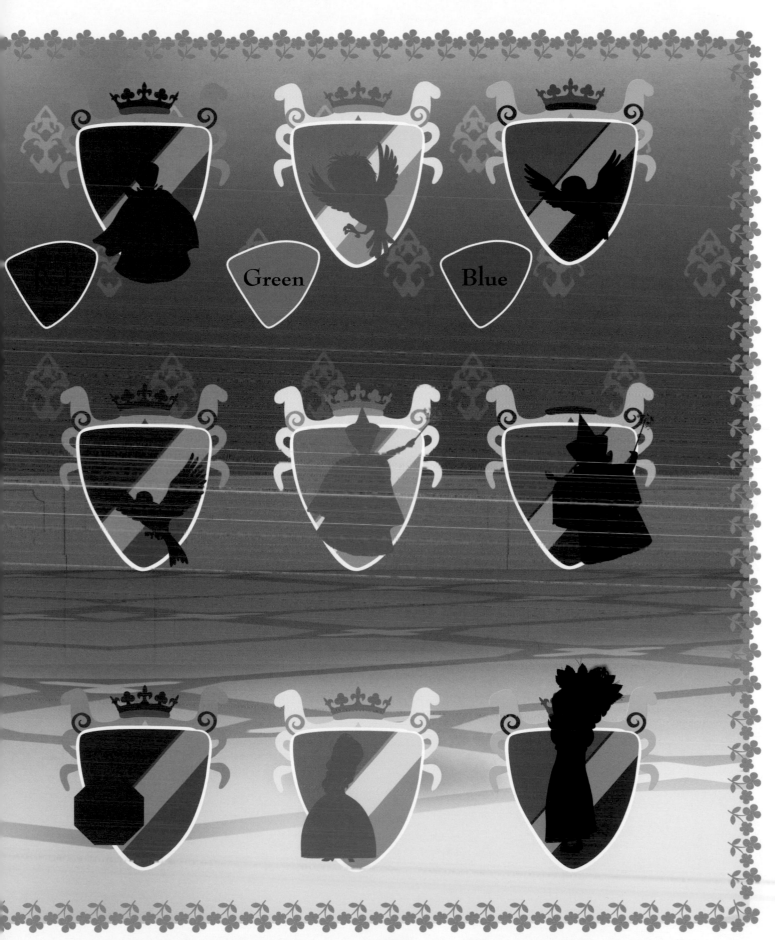

Green

Blue

Complete the Story

The book below tells the story of how Sofia became a princess. Use your stickers to decorate the pages.

Once Upon a Time...

... in Enchancia, a beautiful woman named Miranda lived with her daughter, Sofia. They lived happily together, in the shoe store her mother ran.

One day, Miranda met King Roland, and they fell in love. Once they were married, Sofia and her mother became royalty!

Sofia now had a new family, including a stepsister named Princess Amber. Though they were very different, they soon became friends.

Sofia also had a new stepbrother, Prince James. James loved joking around, but he was also ready to help Sofia learn to be a princess.

King Roland gave Sofia the Amulet of Avalor, which gave her the power to talk to animals! She soon had many new feathered and furry friends.

As a princess, there's a lot for Sofia to learn. She won't learn to act like royalty overnight, but she's excited to be a princess-in-training!

Having a Ball

It's the perfect evening for ballroom dancing. Use your stickers to make the bottom scene look like the top one.

Magic Lessons

Count the Copies

Fauna is teaching the class how to make copies of anything! With your stickers, count the number of copies she has made.

Gem Designs

Help Prince Zandar and Sofia complete the magical pattern below with your stickers.

Curious Crystal Ball

Help Sofia and Amber figure out who's appearing in Cedric's crystal ball.

Lessons in the Library

Sofia's class is in the library today. Decorate the scene with your stickers.

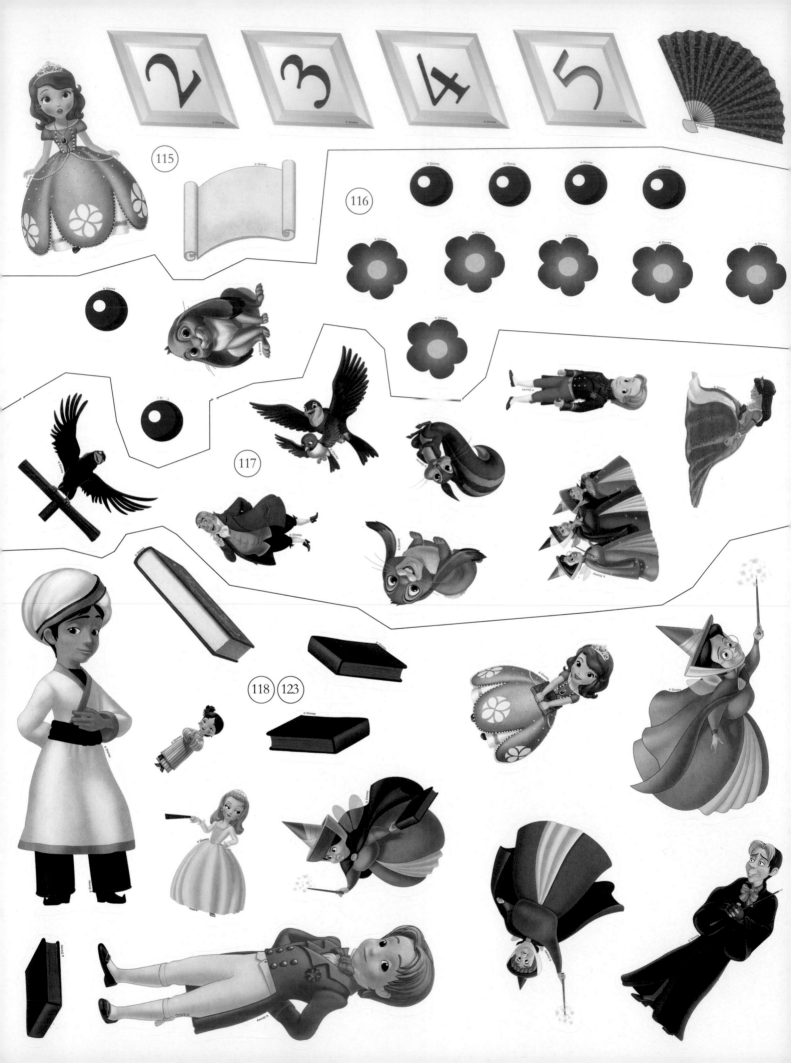

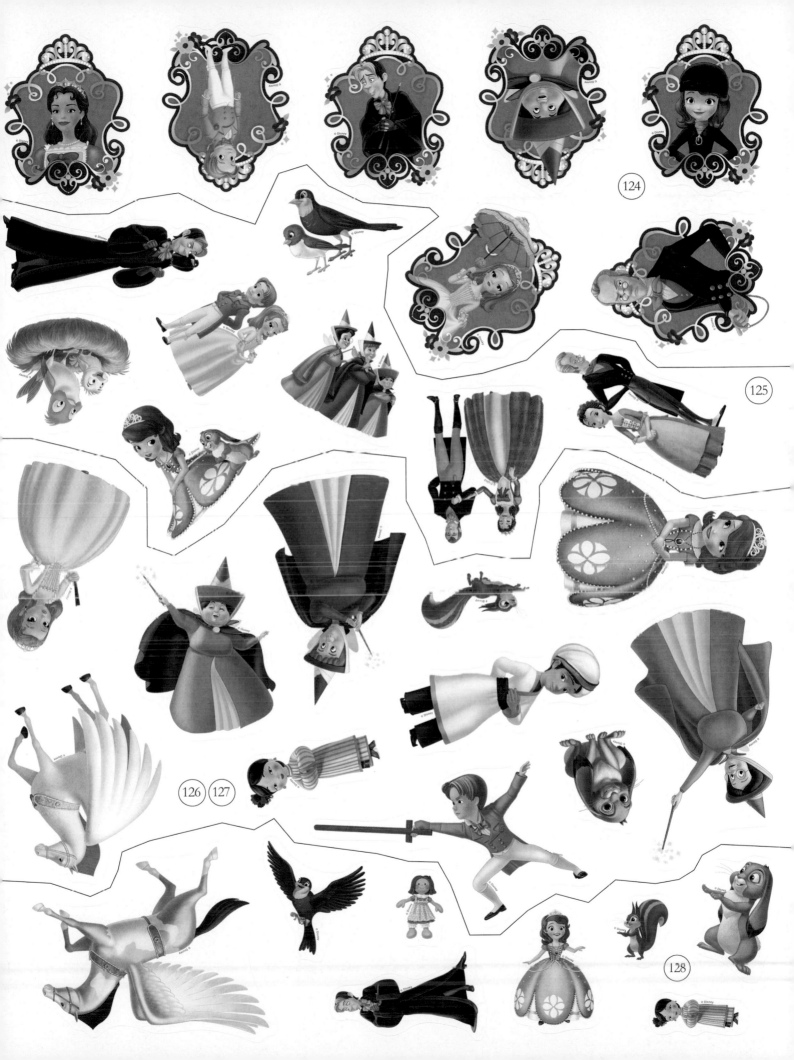

The Finding Spell

This spell helps you find whatever you've lost! Use your stickers to match each character to his or her lost item.

The Mismatch Spell

This spell has matched up the wrong people and animals! Use your stickers to undo the spell.

Can You See Me?

Sofia's class is learning an invisibility spell. Use your stickers to make everyone reappear!

The Mini Spell

Sofia has been practicing a spell to make things little. Match the stickers to the shadows to make everything the correct size.